GHOSTS
OF THE

OZARKS

by

Bruce Carlson

QUIXOTE PRESS

i

****

**QUIXOTE
PRESS**

Printed in U.S.A.

DEDICATION

To all those
bumps in the night,
those things seen
out of the corner
of your eye, and
those little feelings
in the back of your
neck

TABLE OF CONTENTS

FOREWORD

Bruce Carlson has dug deeply
into the rocks of the Ozarks
and the lives of its people
to find these stories of ghosts.

We are fortunate he has spent
those countless hours talking
to the children of hills whose
flying pigtails are now crowns
of grey, and whose young and
supple arms now hold canes and
shawls as their owners recall
the stories of their youth.

Phil Hey
Briar Cliff College

PREFACE

These stories of ghosts of the Ozarks come down through families, some are written down, some are only told.

Now and then a piece of lace, an old photo, or a relic of years ago will be brought out of a dresser drawer, a sugar bowl, or a bank safety deposit box to add to the telling of the story.

What happens when these things are put away again? Are they simply pieces of lace and old photos, or are there things happening that are not for our eyes to see or our ears to hear?

CHAPTER I

THE EXTRA SLEEPER

When Mrs. Brownly of Camdenton, Missouri, died in 1903, she left four small children. Mr. Brownly, of course, had to pick up the slack and be both mother and father to the little ones.

It was kind of tough going for Brian Brownly to do that, but he managed to get those kids raised.

One event that took place shortly after he lost his wife was an unforgettable one.

The children had all gone to bed and he turned in early, having to get some sleep so he could get to work the next day. Having to put in a full day's work plus take care of those kids left little time for anything else.

Brian had just dropped off to sleep when he felt someone crawl into bed next to him. It wasn't uncommon for those kids to do that, so while it was enough to wake him up somewhat, it didn't surprise him.

Brian was awake enough to think that he had better go and check the other kids.

Both girls were fast asleep in their bed and seemed to be all right.

As Brian went down the hall to check the boys' room, he knew that he would find only one of them since the other would be whoever crawled into bed with him and would still be in his room. He idly wondered who it was that had disturbed what had been a good sleep.

Brian's discovery that both boys were in their beds came as a real surprise. Who was in his bed if both girls were asleep in their beds and both boys were in their own room? Whoever it was, they couldn't have gotten back to their room since he never left the hallway and he would have seen them.

Little Timmy Brownly sat up in bed and asked his father what was wrong.

"That's okay, Timmy, go back to sleep. I'll see you in the morning."

Brian touched Timmy's brother to be sure he was there, then stopped at the girls' room again to be sure they were really there. Surely, he had been mistaken. One of them must be in his bed, but no one was. Both girls were sound asleep in their beds.

Brian then decided he must have only dreamed that someone had crawled into bed with him. All four kids were accounted for.

When he got back to his room, he knew that something strange had been going on. The covers on the other side of the bed were thrown back and the pillow was crumpled as if it had been used. Someone had been in that bed! It wasn't his imagination or a dream.

Almost without thinking, Brian's hand found the sheet and he felt it to be warm as if some-one had lain there on that cool evening.

Brian Brownly was fully awake, and thoroughly mystified, wondering what was going on. Someone had been in his bed, and it wasn't one of the kids.

Suddenly it occurred to him what had happened. The pillow had been set on end and used in a way to raise the sleeper's head as much as possible. That was a habit that Mrs. Brownly had had all their married life.

It was Mrs. Brownly who had slipped into that bed and lain beside him for a few minutes.

CHAPTER II

THE READY SHOWER

Some folks will do a good job of keeping themselves well groomed, and others won't.

That's the way it is today, and that was the way it was back when Jeff Reynolds eked out a living doing a little farming outside of Aurora down along the river.

His supplementing his income with a little hunting and fishing was how they got by.

In spite of warnings from the neighbors that it'd "sap his strength", Jeff took a bath every Saturday evening. Sure as clockwork, he'd take his Saturday evening bath.

Actually, I've been a bit inaccurate. Jeff didn't take a bath. Other folks in the community did on occasion, but Jeff didn't. He took a shower.

A shower, of course, was somewhat of a revolutionary idea there around Aurora. The standard procedure was to take baths: outside in a tank in the summer, and in by the stove in a tub in the winter. In most homes,  the tub was set next to the stove so that the water being heated there on the stove didn't have to be carried a long ways. It made for kind of a cozy place to bathe, too.

Jeff's set-up was altogether different. He had him a large steel tank set up outside at the top 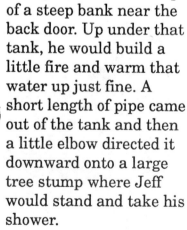 of a steep bank near the back door. Up under that tank, he would build a little fire and warm that water up just fine. A short length of pipe came out of the tank and then a little elbow directed it downward onto a large tree stump where Jeff would stand and take his shower.

Jeff was just more than happy with his rig and

used it fifty-two Saturdays of the year. He didn't let the winter time slow him down any. That warm water was just as warm in January as it was in July. He'd happily scrub down there under that torrent of water, then take off for the house to dry off. That was probably the cleanest tree stump in Lawrence County since it got such a good scrubbing down every week.

Sometimes when the snow was heavy, the only thing that would show up well there in the Reynold's yard was that coal-black tank that would be heated up once a week and wouldn't allow the snow to accumulate on it.

Apparently Jeff's tendency to cleanliness with that bath routine every week didn't do him much good in terms of health. He died at the relatively early age of fifty-eight. One of those neighbors that always wondered why he bathed so often observed there at the general store in Aurora that Jeff might have had all the strength washed right out of him with all those showers.

Jeff died on a Sunday afternoon in early November of 1906 and was buried the following day.

Two of Mrs. Reynold's sisters came to stay with her for a week or so, as was the custom of those days.

By Tuesday it started to snow good and was still going at it by the following afternoon. It was on that Wednesday when one of Mrs. Reynold's sisters was looking out of the kitchen window and noticed the tank there on the bank above the house was free of snow while everything else was hidden beneath a layer of that white stuff. She couldn't understand that and asked Mrs. Reynolds why that tank was not also snow-covered.

Mrs. Reynolds explained the purpose of the tank and suggested that there was probably still some warmth in the water from Jeff's shower on the previous Saturday.

"It's probably still warm enough to melt any snow that lands on it, don't you know?"

The next couple of days indicated that Mrs. Reynolds was undoubtedly right about that. By Friday morning, the snow had stopped but had gotten the tank well covered before it did.

That long snow that week had changed the countryside so that it looked almost like a picture out of a book. Everything was snow-covered, giving the Reynolds place a fairy-take appearance. The three sisters were admiring how pretty it was outside all week.

Come Saturday evening, Mrs. Reynolds' eyes were drawn involuntarily to the window looking out toward her husband's shower. This would be the first Saturday night in many, many years that thing wouldn't be cranked up for his Saturday night shower.

A gasp escaped her lips as she looked out the window.

"Why, Helen, what's the matter?" a sister asked.

"I ......I can't figure it out. Look at that tank of ......of Jeff's."

There in an otherwise snow-covered world was Jeff's tank, just as free of snow as the kitchen table there beside the ladies.

"But, how can that be, Helen?"

The other sister joined the pair at the window

and also saw this strange thing.

"Yes, how can that be? The water is cooled off by now, and no one has built a fire under the tank."

The mystery of what the ladies saw led all three of them to slip on their coats and overshoes and wade out through the snow to the tank.

Even before Mrs. Reynolds put her hand on the tank she knew it was warm. She could feel the warmth radiating from it on to her face.

Again, the three asked each other how that could be since they knew that no one had built a fire under the tank. In fact, they could see in the snow that there had been no tracks leading to or from the tank.

As Mrs. Reynolds was groping for an explanation, her sister quietly said:

"Helen, I think it was Jeff who did this. It was Jeff who built a fire to warm this water. He did that just as he had done for every Saturday for years."

Mrs. Reynolds started to dismiss her sister's idea as being silly and superstitious. The words were lost though, in her realization that her sister was probably right.

Nothing more was said for the next few days about the tank. Within a short time it had cooled down again and a skiff of snow covered it just as it did everything else.

None of the ladies spoke about wondering what would happen the next Saturday, but all of them felt that the next Saturday would either confirm or deny the theory that Jeff's ghost was still with them at the Reynolds farm.

Come the following Saturday, each of the three would casually glance out of the kitchen window on occasion, looking out toward that tank. As the day wore on, it appeared that the tank was no different than anything else out there. It, too, was snow-covered from the earlier skiff of snow.

Along about the middle of the afternoon, Mrs. Reynolds started to become embarrassed that she had allowed herself to think that the incident of a week ago could have been the work of

Jeff's ghost. She wasn't one to believe in that sort of thing and dismissed it all as something brought on by the stress and strain of having just lost her husband.

It was working on toward five o'clock that afternoon, however, when all those brave and logical thoughts were driven from her mind. Suddenly that tank outside stood there coal black without a flake of snow on it.

Helen called her sisters to the window to look at what she saw.

The trio looked at each other. None of them had to explain what was going on. Each knew why the tank was suddenly free of snow. Each knew that what they had talked about a week earlier was true.

Without a word, the three ladies again slipped on their coats and overshoes so they could go back out to the tank.

Mrs. Reynolds didn't know if she wanted to find that tank warm or not. She didn't know if she wanted her husband's ghost to be around or not. It was a long trip, those few yards to the tank.

The two sisters held back and let Helen get to

the tank first. Helen Reynolds hesitated a moment before pulling her glove off and placing her bare hand on the black surface.

The look on Helen's face as her hand rested on that warm tank was all the other two women needed to know that the tank was warm again. It was just as Jeff had done for many years of his life, and now, also for two Saturdays afterwards.

Every Saturday night for almost a year that tank would be warm, all ready for a shower. Through July and August of the following summer, it would be kind of warm all the time, of course. But on Saturday nights it would get even warmer, then cool off again until a week later.

Then, about the middle of September, almost a year after Jeff's death, that strange phenomenon stopped. After that, it was just another tank of water.

That next winter the tank split open from the water inside freezing and breaking the tank. After that, it didn't have any water in it at all.

When Mrs. Reynolds moved away in 1921, the place was bought by another family. The tank was thrown in a ditch along with some other junk and covered up.

CHAPTER III

A TUG ON A TOE

Art Henselman and Jim Swanson started in school together in 1906 in the first grade. They soon became fast friends and re-mained so until Art's death in the fall of 1916.

Those two boys were closer than most brothers those ten years and spent almost all of their waking hours together. If they weren't in school they were busy with the really important stuff like huntin', fishin' and "just messin' around."

The two boys had no concept of the organized and regimented activity that boys years later were to assume was their just due. They wouldn't have known what to do with a Youth Activity Center. They, like other boys of the time, knew that there was the world of kids, and the world of adults.

They instinctively knew that any attempts to combine the two worlds would have been simply another attempt by the adults to control them and otherwise mess up their lives. They knew they were less powerful than "the Growed-Ups" and the only way to survive in their world was to have as little as possible to do with them.

Huntin' and fishin' was, of course, an ideal way to escape the clutches of the "growed-ups" and the two spent a lot of time at those pursuits.

Jim recalls now, over eighty years later, how the two of them would extract those nice carp or bullheads from the Arkansas River outside of town. A favorite way was to use a homemade net. The boys would do enough odd jobs to buy a length of cheesecloth. From that they would fashion a seine some thirty to forty feet long. That long seine, being six feet wide was an ideal way to snag some nice fish. Of course, along with the fish, they would often pull in some crawdaddies, an eel or two, and sometimes a turtle. It was a lot of fun and more exciting than sitting on the bank with a fishin' pole.

When the mood was more contemplative than active, the two would lay on the bank with their feet toward the water. They'd tie their fishing line onto their big toes and lie on their backs, studying the clouds. They could find all sorts of images in those clouds and  rarely tired of watching that ever-changing picture high overhead.

Of course, now, things would get kind of exciting when a sharp tug on a big toe was the signal that they had caught a fish.

"Ya know, Mister," Jim told me while I was interviewing him, "A good-sized carp or bull-head can tug right smartly on a feller's toe. Fact is, one day, I tied into a right large snapper. That turtle headed off for the deep water with my line. That big toe of mine got good and  swollen up by the time we got that line grabbed and took the pull off of it. We used to get some mighty find fish that way, though. Gettin' those nice fish made a sore toe now and then worth it, I guess."

"Whad'd you do with your fish?" I asked Jim.

"Well, mostly, we fried 'em in an iron pot we used to carry our bait in. Now 'n then, we'd take those fish home and give them to our folks. They'd always be glad to get a nice mess of fish sometimes. It kind of kept 'em out of our hair, don't ya know."

 By this time, I had started to wonder what all this talk of fish and old iron pots had to do with ghosts. I had been told he knew about a ghost, but I sure hadn't heard anything yet that sounded like a ghost story!

"Well, I tell ya, it happened in 1916. I was seventeen years old that summer and was all up in a lather 'bout joinin' the army. There was the war goin' on ya know, and there I was already seventeen. My Pa told me, tho, in no uncertain terms that I was goin' to finish High School. Lots of fellows weren't goin' all the way through High School back then, ya know. But Pa said I had to.

 That summer I was seventeen was a bad one. Not only was I awantin' to be in the army so bad, but it was that summer that Art got killed in a car wreck. It was the first summer I could ever remember being without Art, and I sure

didn't care for it. We was awful good buddies for a long, long time, ya know. So, I was pretty much alone after that. And I was all alone one day when I went out to the old fishin' hole, hopin' to land me a nice bullhead.

Jus' like Art 'n me used to do, I'd tied my line off on to my toe, thinkin' about Art, 'n goin' in the army, n' all.

Jus' about then I felt this tug on my toe and heard my name called out at the same time. That tug was nothin' special, of course, but I sure couldn't figure who had called out my name. It kind of shook me up 'cause it sounded jus' like Art's voice.

After looking 'round for a while trying ta figure out where that voice was comin' from, I turned back to that line. I kind of figured I had me a nice fish, ya know."

"And, did you have one there on your line?" I asked.

Jim kind of chuckled as he answered.

"Ya know, after I'd tied that line onto my toe, I had gave it a toss to get it out into the water, and ya know what?"

"No, what?" I asked.

"That dang line had snagged up on a branch in the box elder tree overhead, and I never had gotten that line anywhere near the water. That whole line, including hook and bait was out of the water all that time. A lot of it was right up in the branches of that tree I was layin' under."

"But I thought you said you felt a tug on it."

"I sure did, and I heard my name called out, too."

"But", I asked, "How could it have gotten tugged on, if it wasn't even out in the water?"

"Well, I knowed as soon as I seen that line up in the tree that it was Art that had been a tuggin' on that and hollering out my name. I guess that was his way of spending one last lazy summer afternoon with me.

"A lotta years have gone by since then. I can't say that I've ever tied off a fishin' line on my toe since then. I know, though, that if I did, I'd probably hear from Art again. We wuz good buddies, ya know."

CHAPTER IV

THE GLOWING HAYSTACK

This story goes way back to the 1880s, and was supposed to have happened on a farm between Mountain View, Arkansas and Melbourne. The old gal who told me the story didn't know the name of the farmer, or even the exact year. She said she had been to the farm when she was a small child, but that was thirty years after the event. She got the story from her father who said he had been a witness to it all.

"Even when I was there, it was kind of a ram-shackly place, and that was a long time ago. I 'spect the buildings are all gone by now."

"So, what happened?" I asked.

The following is an account of what this woman told me.

It was in June and the farmer had just gotten done putting up his hay. Like others, this guy had put it up in huge haystacks right out there in the field. That was long before balers, of

course, so that's about the only way they could do it. As they would need the hay, they would either haul it in to feed the cattle, or let them eat it right out there.

About two or three days after the farmer had

built a large stack there in the hayfield, he
woke up one night to the sounds of a neighbor
who was pounding on his door to tell him his
haystack was on fire.

The man knew there wasn't a whole lot a guy
could do after a haystack got to burning good,
but he threw on his clothes to go out to see what
it was all about, anyway.

When the two men got there, they
found the stack wasn't on fire after
all, but it sure had something odd
going on about it. The stack
glowed like it had a thousand
lanterns blazing away on the inside of it. Glow-
ing haystacks aren't the commonest things, of
course, so the two men stood there a long time
and watched it. That stack just glowed for all it
was worth, putting out more than enough light
to cast strong shadows.

Both men were at a total loss to understand
how such a thing could be. Even as they stood
there talking about it, however, the glow
seemed to fade, and was then gone.

The next morning the farmer poked and
prodded around in that stack to see if he could
determine just what was going on. He found
nothing in spite of running a pitchfork deep into

the stack.

Word got around pretty fast, or course. That
next night there were two or three dozen people
at that stack to see for themselves what they
had heard about.

That night, and for several more, that stack
looked no different than any other. It was about

a week later when
the same thing
happened again.
The farmer saw
it himself first
that time.

This guy was
smarting a
little under
some criticism
about his imagining it all, so he hurried up and
got some neighbors over to look at it.

Sure enough, it was doing the same thing it had
done the week before. This time, however,
enough people saw it that it became believable
again. Once more a crowd gathered each night
for a few days. A few days later, the group on
watch were rewarded with the sight of the glow-
ing haystack for the third time.

That was the last time it happened. There were
lots of theories as to what had caused the glow.

The most common one that there was some kind of electricity in the air that did it. Electricity was still enough of a novelty that people were about prepared to believe just about anything having to do with that mysterious stuff.

The farmer enjoyed a period of fame for being the man with the electrical haystack there for a while.

It was that winter when people changed their minds about the cause of that glow. For it was then when the farmer was feeding the hay and discovered the remains of a body down under the stack. There was a bullet hole through the man's head, so he was assumed to have been the victim of a murder. It was theorized that someone had decided to bury the evidence of a murder by putting the body in a stack the day the farmer was unloading load after load of hay onto it. A handgun was also found lying by the body.

My source of this story didn't know if they ever figured out who the victim was or if the murderer was ever caught.

Whoever the poor fellow was, he apparently had a ghost in the form of light.

CHAPTER V

A LITTLE BIT OF GRANDPA

Old Man Seerman was the elderly father of Wally Seerman who lived there on the home place west of Harrison, Arkansas a few miles. Old Man Seerman lived in the old family home with his son Wally and Wally's wife Victoria.

The old man enjoyed his last years there on the farm. He could do a little work, or none at all, whatever suited his fancy on any particular day

The old feller had his own room in the loft of their modest home, so he had plenty of privacy. Wally and Victoria's two sons had their sleeping quarters in what was little more than a large walk-in closet on the main floor.

The two boys were sorry to see their grandfather die in 1921, but it did provide th opportunity for them to move up into the loft in the

nice room that old man lived in all those years.
Both the boys were glad to be able to make that
move to better sleeping quarters.

Old Man Seerman died in April, just about
when life on a farm starts getting pretty busy.
With all the work to be done, little got
accomplished in terms of rearranging the furniture in the boys' new room. In fact, most of their
grandfather's effects were stuffed into the
drawers of his big old bureau since the boys had
their own chest of drawers.

It happened the very first night the boys slept up in that room. Along about eleven o'clock that night one of the boys heard a click......click...... click sound over from the far end of the room. He listened to that quite a while before shaking his brother awake to listen to it, too.

The boys lay in bed and speculated for some time about what could be making that noise. They finally decided that a mouse was working on the paper lining in the drawers of their bureau and was snapping the edges of the paper against the inside of the drawer.

They were a bit concerned that the critter might mess up some of their things in the drawer but decided to let him have his fun for that night, and they'd set a trap for him the next day.

Things like setting traps for mice are easy to forget in the morning, however. Both of the boys forgot about their unwanted guest until the next night when they heard that click .... click...........again.

That got to be too much. Those boys had some good stuff in there and sure didn't need it chewed up by some dang mouse.

As the boys sneaked over to the bureau with a rolled-up newspaper, they hoped to send that mouse to mouse heaven with a couple good whacks. They discovered, however, the noise wasn't coming from their bureau at all. It was coming from their grandfather's that was setting next to their own.

When the fellows tried to listen closely to see which drawer their mouse was in, the sound suddenly stopped and then they could find nothing. They thought the sound was coming from the top drawer. On inspection, however, all they could find was the old man's pipes, some small change, a couple of combs, and their grandfather's false teeth.

A trap set the next morning accomplished nothing. The third night between eleven o'clock and quarter after that click........click............ click.............. sound started up again.

This time the boys were ready, each of them armed with a short section of a good stout yardstick. They knew they could make short work of that mouse with a good crack of that piece of wood.

Again, the boys located the sound as coming from the top dresser drawer. One of the fellows was going to pull it open quickly while the other was poised to bring his wrath down on their furry little friend.

As that drawer was jerked open, everything went flying to the back. The combs, the change, the false teeth, and the pipes all careened to the back where they rocked and spun around a bit before coming to rest.

As those things in that drawer did that, the boys looked in vain for the mouse. Even as those various objects came to a standstill, however, they heard a click or two. Those false teeth had clicked together a couple of times from all the commotion.

Both boys recognized that clicking sound to be the same that they had heard for the last three nights. They recalled, then, how their grandfather used to click his teeth together as some people are apt to do. It was the same sound.

What would have made those teeth do that all by themselves was beyond the understanding of the stout pair of mouse hunters. It wasn't the sort of thing a little rodent would be likely to make happen.

On the fourth night when that now-familiar sound came from that bureau, one of the boys mentioned the possiblity of their grandfather's ghost doing that with the old set of false teeth in his bureau.

What to do? What to do? Wally and Victoria had some very, very strong opinions on such matters. They were absolutely opposed to talk of supernatural beings. The boys knew they'd be in for big trouble if they suggested the possibility of their Dad's father showing up as a ghost.

The boys didn't know what to do about the whole problem. In the back of their minds was,  of course, the fact that nighttime would come again. They wondered what was going to happen at a little past eleven o'clock that night.

They didn't have to wonder for very long. Come close to midnight that night, the same thing happened again. There was that click .... click .... click .... sound coming from their grandfather's bureau. This time the boys knew what it was and spent a good deal of the night with their heads under the covers.

Come morning both boys were pretty tired. They hadn't slept well, having a ghost in their bedroom with them.

Morning also brought a welcome sight, however.

It was raining. The fellows knew that the rain would bring their father's plowing to a halt. Maybe they could get their folks to spend that rainy day clearing Grandfather's things out of the bedroom. It worked. Wally and Victoria got talked into going up and redoing the bedroom upstairs.

The drawers of the bureau were emptied and the contents got either pitched out or stuck into an old cupboard out in the summer kitchen. The bureau itself was moved to Wally and Victoria's room and the boys were rid of their problem.

Neither of the boys ever found out what happened to those false teeth and never wanted to know. Perhaps they are still in a box somewhere, going click......click......click...... in the middle of the night.

CHAPTER VI

TORN SCREENS

In the early 1940s, Harold and Annie Stillman fell heir to a large and beautiful old victorian home on the outskirts of Little Rock.

The house had been built by Annie's grandfather in the 1880s. After the old man had died, Annie's aunt and uncle lived in the home for several years. It was known that Annie would inherit the place, even while her aunt and uncle were living there. She got the house as well as its contents, so it was really completely furnished when Harold and Annie moved in in 1942. There were even horse drawn vehicles in the garage, towels in the bathrooms and pictures on the walls. The house was decorated and furnished much like it had been since it was built.

Annie's aunt and uncle kept it that way because of the requirements of the arrangements under which they lived there. Annie planned to keep it that way because she liked antiques and eagerly antici-pated the opportunity to live in a home that looked like it was still back in the nine-teenth century.

The house was typical of old Victorian homes in that it had the large cupola onthe top, the tall narrow windows, and a large porch that went around two sides of the house.

It was different in one respect in that the porch was screened in. The practice of screening in the porch of that style of house is not totally unknown, but only infrequently done. It tends to detract from the overall appearance of such a house, so the porch is usually left open. But not this one. The uncle had gotten some carpenters in and had them build screens for the entire two sections. It was generally considered to have been a mistake in that it made a beautiful old house look kind of dumpy and odd.

That situation wasn't helped any by the condi-tion of the screens. When Harold and Annie moved in, the screens were torn, bulged, and loosened from their frames. That was kind of a surprise since her uncle had kept the rest of the place immaculate. Neither Howard or Annie could figure why he allowed those screens to be in such a bad condition.

That issue had to take a back seat to many others in those first few weeks of living in their new house. There was the moving in itself, the rearrangement of the furniture, putting in a new furnance, seeding down the garden spot they had no interest in using, etc.

By then, winter came and the weather wasn't fit to do anything with those tacky old screens.

Annie's expectation that she would really enjoy living in what was almost a museum turned out to be justified. She and her husband really loved their new home just the way it was, even so far as to leave the pictures hanging on the walls where they found them. They particularly enjoyed the large oil paintings of Annie's grandparents that hung in the stairway. The paintings had been done by a professional and gave the home a rich and genteel atmosphere. The fact that Annie's grandfather looked as sour as if he had just eaten a pickle didn't detract from how nice those old portraits looked. Every now and then the couple would joke about how sour Annie's grandfather looked in that gold gilt frame in the stairway.

By spring, Harold was anxious to get started repairing the screens on the porch. He didn't really care for the screened-in porch; but if he was going to have one, it was going to look good.

So all the old screens came out, the frames repaired and repainted. New screen was put back in. It looked pretty good, but only for a day. The next morning that new screen was torn, bulged, wrinkled in spots, and rusty.

It was immediately assumed that some vandals had done a number on that screen in the night. In fact, an insurance claim was submitted on that basis. Harold was a little mystified about the rusty spots. He had difficulty in figuring out how the screen wire could have rusted just overnight. He just chalked that up to poor materials and got some carpenters in to do the whole job over again.

The same thing happened the next night. That second set of screens looked like it had been there for years by the next morning.

Being a man of some influence in town, Harold was able to see that a police car was watching the home the day after the carpenters re-placed that second set of screens with a third.

But, again, it was a mess in the morning.

By this time Harold was mad, the police were involved, and the insurance agent was making hints about there being a limit to the extent to which the insurance company would go.

Other attempts to shape up that porch met with the same results. Finally, in desperation, Harold ripped the wire out, removed the frames, filled the nail holes with putty and repainted the whole porch. He figured it was better to get rid of that whole issue than to keep fighting whatever the problem was.

From that time on, there was never again any evidence of any vandalism of the Stillman house. Neighbors and other townspeople re-marked at how much better the house looked showing off the porch as it should have been left in the first place.

Harold and Annie were pretty proud of the improved appearance of their house. Harold said that he wished he had done that in the first place, rather than to try to repair that tacky mess.

There was one part of the situation that Harold and Annie never mentioned to anyone outside the family, however. They also strongly instructed their two children to say nothing about it. In fact, Mrs. Evans, their daughter, breathed not a word of it until she told me a few months ago, fifty years after the fact.

What Mrs. Evans told me was that the very day that her father removed the wire and frames, there was a sudden and unexplainable change in the oil painting of her great-grandfather that hung in the stairway. From that day on, his sour look was gone and his face almost had a hint of a smile on it.

"Are you telling me that the old gent's face in that oil painting changed when your father took that screen down?" I asked.

"That's true, my brother and I both saw it. My mother and father talked about it. I know that it happened and I know that it happened right after my father removed that screen. Furthurmore, I'm convinced that great-grandfather disliked that screen and it was he that did the vandalism. I mean, it was his ghost that did it. I know it would be a weird situation, but then what other explanation would there be for a change in his face in the painting?"

Maybe Mrs. Evans is right. Maybe we all have to take a new look at those seemingly dead old portraits hanging on our walls. Maybe those faces frozen in time are more than simply smears of oil.

CHAPTER VII

PADDY O'NEIL

There are lots of Irishmen called "Paddy". In fact, it's kind of a generic name for any man from The Emerald Isle, whatever his given name.

Paddy O'Neil was a shopkeeper in Fayetteville, Arkansas for many years. He got along just fine with his name and was kind of proud of it, for it showed off his Irish ancestory. In fact, his grandfather, Paddy O'Neil, was a small farmer back in Ireland so that name suited him just fine.

It was, however, a whole lot different when Paddy was growing up back in Boston. Paddy's parents appar-  ently didn't know how to spell the name they hung on their son. His birth certificate clearly showed his name to be Patty O'Neil.

Now having to face those tough Irish kids in school when your name was a bit odd was bad enough on the boy. To have to live with a girl's name was a whole lot worse. Paddy's children in Fayetteville were convinced that the trouble their father had had in Boston with his name was probably the reason he had come to Arkansas in the first place.

Here in Fayetteville, Patty was immediately changed to Paddy unofficially. The birth certificate, school records, and military records still, of course, showed the "Patty" his folks had cursed him with.

Paddy's wife and children knew that he was using a spelling of his name that wasn't as given him, but no one else in the area knew. All they knew was that his name was Paddy O'Neil.

Paddy died in 1940. Being a veteran of World War I, he qualified for a tombstone furnished by the U.S. Army. Mrs. O'Neil thought that Paddy would have liked to have been recognized for his service as a soldier, so she notified the proper authorities for the stone to be prepared by the government.

Probably no one in the government bureaucracy cared one whit about the fact that Private O'Neil had a girl's name. They just had the job done and sent the stone to the funeral home. The funeral director had his men install the stone on Paddy's grave.

There it was . . . . "Patty O'Neil".

Mrs. O'Neil hadn't even thought about the fact that those army records would have the correct spelling of the name, a spelling that Paddy had hated from the time he was a child.

When the funeral director told her the stone was in place, she went to see it. She immediately realized that she had a problem. She didn't want to have to go through the agony of a new stone being prepared, but she knew that

Paddy wouldn't have liked that correct spelling of his name on the stone one little bit.

Mrs. O'Neil mulled over the problem all that evening and still hadn't decided what to do about it come the next morning.

That afternoon two of her children were going to go out to see the stone so Mrs. O'Neil decided to go along. She told them about the name-spelling situation on the way out and told them that she didn't know yet, what she was going to do about it.

When the party got to the cemetery, they all walked up the little knoll to where Paddy's grave was located. There was that stone, just as Mrs. O'Neil had seen it the day before. That is, it was almost like she had seen it the day before. The only difference was that the "Patty" was changed to "Paddy".

This all caught Mrs. O'Neil by surprise. She was sure that it had been spelled correctly the previous day, but here it was spelled the way Paddy would have wanted. How could that be?

Mrs. O'Neil's children were convinced that their mother was suffering delusions. They felt that she had been under a strain and that she had only imagined that. Mrs. O'Neil insisted, however, that the stone was different than it had been the day before.

To humor their mother, her son Sean told her he'd write to the Army people and ask them how they had spelled the name on the stone.

"You'll see, Mother, that they will tell us that they spelled it just the way it shows on there now."

The next few days were busy ones so the issue was pretty much forgotten until the answer came back from the Army. They told the O'Neils that the stone had been processed according to their records, and that the name was *Patty O'Neil*.

It was then that the family knew what had happened. The only possible explanation was that Paddy himself had changed the inscription to what he wanted.

CHAPTER VIII

PAYING OFF THE LOAN

Vance Redman's death in 1947 in Springfield, Missouri, wasn't noticed by many people in town. Vance was kind of a loner with no relatives and very few friends. He lived in a tumbled-down shack he didn't even own there on the edge of town.

At the time of his death it was discovered that the shack was on ground owned by the highway. The highway people hadn't even known that.

Vance's wordly belongings were both few and of very little value so there wasn't enough to bury Vance without resorting to county funds to do so.

The authorities found, among his belongings, a record showing a modest loan at a local bank. On checking that out, it was learned that there was indeed such a loan in force.

Vance had maintained a good record of making the payments on the loan, but the bank officers realized they would never see the balance of the money. There was almost a hundred dollars yet owed. The bank wrote it off as being uncollectable.

Almost twenty years went by until the late 1960s when a man came into the bank to inquire about the status of his loan. He quoted a loan number and told the girl he wanted to "settle up" that loan.

The girl's search of the records showed that there was no loan of that identification outstanding. The man insisted, however, and wouldn't leave until the folks at the bank came up with a figure so he could pay them off.

The increasingly distraught teller finally
summoned a bank officer to straighten things
out. The old man simply wouldn't hear anything
about there being no such loan.

The officer had a lot of difficulty figuring out
what was going on. It was almost by accident
that he ran through the old numbers of loans
that had been written off as uncollectable.
There he found it.

The accumulated interest hadn't even been
calculated since the loan was considered dead,
and the officer went through the figures and
came up with a new balance.

The stranger produced some bills and change
and paid the loan off, down to the very last
penny.

The thing that caught the bank officer's eye was that the change the old duffer gave him included several of the old 1943 zinc-colored pennies. By the late 1960s those pennies simply weren't seen anymore. Yet the old man had several among the money he paid the bank that day.

The event of that old man coming to the bank and raising all that commotion about a "dead" loan cause somewhat of a stir among the bank employees that day. There was quite a bit of talk among them at coffee break that next morning.

One of the old female employees who hadn't been at work the previous day wasn't paying  a whole lot of attention to the discussion about the old man.

She got real interested pretty soon, though, as the girl described the old man for the benefit of the others there at the coffee table.

Her interest was piqued because the girl's description of the old man was such that it sounded like Vance Redman whom the woman had known years earlier.

She asked the girl some questions about the old guy. The girl's responses included a description of a large purple wart on his right temple. That was enough to cinch it. The woman knew that it had to have been Vance Redman who came in the day before.

Somehow, Vance Redman, or his ghost, came in to pay the loan off. Since Vance had been dead for about twenty years, it had to have been his ghost.

Maybe it makes sense for a man's ghost to want to pay off an old debt, but one had to wonder about a couple of things. Why did he wait so long? And where did he get that old money?

CHAPTER IX

THE FLICKERING LIGHTS

In 1947, a young man, driving along was killed when he missed a curve in the road south of Jefferson City, Missouri. The fellow was from out of town, so it didn't take long for the death of that stranger to be pretty well forgotten there in the community.

The Watson family who lived there on that curve didn't forget it however. To have a man lose his life in their front yard wasn't the sort of thing the Watsons got over very fast.

In fact, it was the Watsons who first saw the poor fellow lying dead in his car. They had just settled down for an evening of making candy and popcorn when the accident happened. Their first knowledge that anything was amiss was

when the lights suddenly went off. That was
immediately followed by the strange sounds of a
crashing automobile. The car had broken the
pole in their front yard and severed the wires
leading to the house.

The whole family rushed out into the yard to
see what had happened, and it was then they
discovered the tragedy of the young fellow's
death.

The rest of the evening was devoted to a lot
more than candy and popcorn. The police came,
reporters were taking pictures, and several
neighbors gathered there in the yard. The
power company came, of course, to restore
power to the house.

The young fellow's
remains were
taken away and a
wrecker came the
next morning for
the car. Within a
couple of days, all
that remained to
show there had
been an accident there was a new light pole
and some scars in the grass where the car had
gouged holes. Mr. Watson filled with these with
dirt and reseeded the area.

The months passed by and life had returned to

normal at the Watson home. The children would still talk about the accident on occasion, but no one had any idea that the incident wasn't quite over.

It was in the early evening and the Watsons were all seated at the supper table. Suddenly the lights flickered, momentarily went out, then came back on again. This seemed strange since it wasn't a stormy evening, nor was there any wind at all.

The next morning Mrs. Watson mentioned that incident to the neighbors, thinking they must have noticed the same thing. Neither of the neighbors had, however, noticed any flickering of the lights the evening before.

Since Mrs. watson neither understood how electricity worked, nor cared, she soon forgot the incident.

A year later it happened again. When the lights flickered the second time that way in the absence of any storm or wind, Mrs. Watson recalled the first time it happened. She then realized that it had been exactly a year, to the day, between the two events. She thought it was really odd that such an unlikely event should happen twice, and on the same day of the year. Mrs. Watson talked about the situation with her family, wondering how that could be.

All she got from the rest of the family was some friendly digs about not having enough to do if she made a habit of keeping track of what date the lights in the house would flicker.

"Just you wait. It will happen again in exactly a year from now."

Mrs. Watson dutifully made a note of the date and promised that she would have the last laugh in a year when it would happen again.

She got some teasing about her "mystery" as the anniversary of those two events approached. Her husband had a lot of fun telling the kids that their mother was losing her grip on reality. The kids picked up on that, of course, and made a big deal out of the coming date "When Mama would have the last laugh."

Come the big day, it happened again, right on

schedule, the same time of evening and all.

Now that was a real surprise to Mr. Watson and the kids. She had called it right on the money. The family talked a lot about it, wondering what was going on.

Their answer came the next day when Mrs. Watson made a trip down to the newspaper office to check on the date of the car wreck. She had a sneaking idea that it was about the same time of year. Sure enough, that was the date of the wreck. All of those three years since the car wreck, the lights had flickered at the same time of evening on the anniversary of that tragic event.

Every year after that the lights in the Watson home would flicker on the anniversary of that wreck. Other than during an occasional storm, those were the only times it would happen.

Did that young man have to relive the night of his death every year on its anniversary? Was it his ghost, marking the time and place of his death? We just don't know.

CHAPTER X

OUTWITTING A GHOST

"Corporal Paton reporting, Sir."

Again that same sentence came filtering into Mrs. Belton's sleepiness.

"Corporal Paton reporting, Sir."

The second time she heard that sentence, Mrs. Belton realized that those words were spoken to her.

The Beltons had expected that their new house might hold some surprises for them, but they expected that those surprises would be things like leaky faucets or maybe a mouse or two.

They sure hadn't expected that their first night there would be interrupted by a total stranger standing in the bedroom.

Besides that, Mrs. Belton wasn't accustomed to being addressed as "Sir".

As sleep left, Mrs. Belton sat up in bed so she could see what was going on. It was then that she saw the young soldier standing over by the door.

The idea of his being a ghost didn't occur to Mrs. Belton at first. He seemed much too real for that. The lad was not ill-defined or etheral in any way. He looked as real as anyone else who might be standing there in the bedroom in the middle of the night. Mrs. Belton even heard what she figured was an old-fashioned pocket

watch the lad must have been carrying.

Automatically, she reached over to wake her husband. She didn't care if their visitor was only a lad in a Civil War uniform that looked about two sizes too large for him. She had little enthusiasm for a stranger in their bedroom.

Mr. Belton's reaction was "What the ....?" just before the soldier evaporated into nothingless.

The couple compared notes that evening. The next morning they talked about it again and agreed that what they had seen was a young soldier in the uniform of the Union Army from back in the days of the Civil War. They also agreed that what they saw must have been a ghost of some nature rather than a mortal.

The idea of a ghost in their new home in West Plains was a bit discomforting to the Beltons. That "new" house was actually only new to them. It was actually already over a hundred years old when they encountered their midnight intruder in 1938.

Since it was an old house, it occurred to the Beltons that it was an ideal home for a ghost. They just weren't convinced they wanted one around.

Mrs. Belton spent the next day studying about their house and the neighborhood in the local library. At no time did she run into the name "Paton". She paid particular attention to the time around the Civil War in hopes of running into that name. The closest thing she found was a Potine family that had lived in the home in the early 1980s.

The Corporal Paton issue pretty much got lost in the following months while the Beltons worked on redoing their new home.

It was almost a year later on a Sunday afternoon. Mrs. Belton was taking a nap while her husband was over to the neighbors on an errand. Suddenly there were those words again.

"Corporal Paton reporting, Sir. Corporal Paton reporting, Sir."

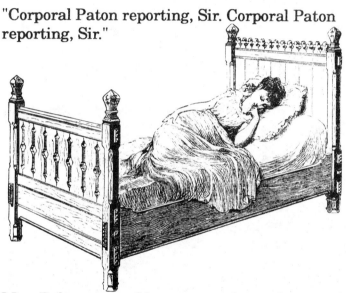

Mrs. Belton opened her eyes and saw the same young soldier standing in the same spot again. Her first instinct was to sit up in bed and to demand to know what he was doing there. Fortunately, however, she suddenly decided on a different course of action. She wondered if she could get the lad to leave some evidence of his having been there.

"Young man, please put your gloves there on the dresser."

Even as she spoke those words she was shocked that she would be talking to a ghost, or whatever he was. Those words escaping her lips seemed to confirm that all this was actually going on. This made her suddenly afraid. It was with some difficulty that she managed to compose herself to keep from screaming and bolting from the room. She said later that she felt she had gained some courage from the fact that it all happened in broad daylight.

Without hesitation, the boy removed his gloves from his belt and placed them on the dresser as she had instructed. His apparent willingness to do her bidding gave Mrs. Belton additional courage.

"Thank you. Now, please, walk to the window by the closet."

That little ploy was designed to put as much distance as possible between the soldier and his gloves. When the lad took his place over by the window as she had told him, she then got between him and his gloves.

More for the feeling of protection it offered than

anything else, Mrs. Belton picked up a cane
that leaned against the wall by the head of the
bed.

Without a word, Mrs. Belton then walked to the
foot of the bed as if she was going to cross the
room to the lad. At that, the young fellow
disappeared as before.

Now was the moment of truth. Would the gloves
be there on the dresser when she turned around
to look at them? Would there be that evidence
that the fellow had been there?

Mrs. Belton told me that she was half afraid
that they would be there and half afraid that
they wouldn't.

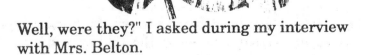

Well, were they?" I asked during my interview
with Mrs. Belton.

"Yes, they were. I went to the dresser, keeping
my eye on those gloves, half-way expecting
them to disappear into thin air as I approached
them. But they didn't. They looked like any

80

other objects, just as real as could be. I looked
at them for a couple of minutes before I touched
them, but I finally did.

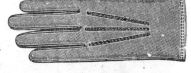

I could hardly wait for
Larry to get home from
the neighbor's. I
decided not to talk to him about it until he was
actually there to see the gloves for fear that
they might disappear before he got home."

"So, did they disappear before he saw them?"

"No, they didn't. When he walked in, I showed
them to him and told him about how I got
them."

Mrs. Belton went on to tell how this second
sighting of the ghost led to a renewed search for
a connection between this soldier and the history of their home. The owners of the home during the Civil War proved to be a family by the
name of Smythe. Mrs. Smythe's maiden name
was Paton. Some genealogical research back in
the library revealed that Mrs. Symthe's brother
was a Corporal Paton in the Union Army, but he
had lost his life in a skirmish shortly after
enlisting.

That information was found in a bound volume in the local library that contained copies of the abstracts of various of the old houses in West Plains.

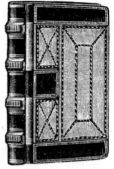

It took a lot of doing, but Mrs. Belton was able to track down an old photograph that relatives of the Smythes had. It was a photograph of a group of people, including young Paton when he was but fourteen years old. That was before he went into the Army, of course, but Mrs. Belton could still see enough of a resemblance between that boy and her ghost that she knew it was he that had stood in their bedroom twice.

The Beltons never could find a good explanation why the young soldier's ghost would want to haunt the house of his sister and her husband. Maybe he had come to their place to recuperate from his wounds and died there. We just don't know.

Mrs. Belton anticipated my next question just before I was able to ask it.

"And, no. I'm sorry, but we don't have those gloves anymore. I sure wish I still had them, but I don't."

"What happened to them?" I asked.

"I wish I knew. I stuck them in a large old trunk in the attic. It was quite a while after that when I had occasion to get into that trunk and found them to be gone."

"Do you suppose that Corporal Paton got into tht trunk and got his property back?" I asked.

"Well", she laughed. "That thought occurred to me too, but I don't know."

CHAPTER XI

THE GARDNER'S RETURN

For many years a small country church not too far from the little town of Mansfield, Missouri, had an interesting tradition.

The tradition was providing of groceries from the church garden to needy folks in the community. It was a big garden and well cared for so it was able to see a lot of people over a temporary problem of not having enough to eat when things got a little tough.

The gardener was an ancient Indian who had come to the community as a relatively young man many years earlier.

This fellow had an unpronounceable name that no one even tried to master so he was simply referred to as Hank.

Hank's sole participation in the affairs of the church was the tending of that garden. He was an ideal man for the job for he seemed to have the proverbial green thumb and was able to make that plot of ground yield just untold quantities of tomatoes, squash, beans, and all the other goodies that a good gardener could coax from the earth. He was said to have used many of the old practices of his people.

Hank had little time to spare for chatting with the folks in the community, so no one really knew why he persisted in a strange practice. His odd habit was to use a hoe made in the fashion of that used by his people for centuries. The hoe was a simple stick on the end of which was lashed the dried and hardened shell of a turtle.

Apparently Hank's hoe was one of those things that came out of the culture that he had left as a young man.

The good Reverend there at the church offered Hank a nice steel hoe for his work, but Hank wanted no part of it. In fact there were two or three regular hoes in the garden shed, but Hank insisted on using his turtle-shell hoe.

Hank was able to do a real number on the weeds in the church garden with that turtle-shell hoe. He would pick his way down the long rows of the garden with a "chop-chop-chop" that would lay waste to any weeds that dared to violate his plot.

There are differences of opinion in the area as to exactly what happened to Hank. One story goes that he fell victim to foul play of some sort or other. Another version is that he simply went to bed one night in his shack and died in his sleep.

It was a couple of days after Hank's death when the Parson remembered that he would have to get someone else to do the garden work. It was in early June and he knew those weeds would get the upper hand pretty soon if he didn't find a replacement for Hank. Things being awfully busy at the time, however, the Parson forgot that detail in the rush of getting other things done.

About a week passed before the good Parson remembered, again, the need to arrange for someone else to do that garden work. He realized, to his dismay, that there would be a real mess in that garden. Weeds worried about grow fast, but weeds forgotten seem to race each other out of the ground. Such is the nature of things.

The preacher hurried down the back lane to the garden, wondering if there would be anything left to salvage in the garden. He felt badly about forgetting that garden and especially so, know-ing how much a nice neat garden had meant to Hank. As he was rushing out there, he was thinking that the only good part of the whole situation was that Hank would have no way of knowing how his precious garden had been neglected.

What the preacher saw when he rounded the bend by the creek was not a tangle of weeds and brush as he had expected, but a garden just as neat as it could be, with nary a weed in it.

The soil between the rows was well-tilled, all of it freshly hoed. Down between those long rows were clumps of dirt, each one in the shape of the inside of a turtle shell as they would do when Hank would hoe with his antique implement.

The preacher was unable to account for how it could be. The only explanation was that it was done by that old hoe of Hank's, and he knew that was locked up in Hank's shack.

The Parson and a couple of the parishioners from the church went to Hank's shack to investigate and found the hoe right there in the corner by the fireplace where Hank had set it the day he last went to bed.

It was then that the good Parson realized that, while he might have forgotten that garden for a week or so, the ghost of Hank hadn't.

CHAPTER XII

UNDER THE HOOVES

All of us know of tragic situations in which a good man loses everything for reasons that are not of his own making.

So it was with Carl Williams who farmed a hundred and twenty acres south of Eureka Springs, Arkansas, in the 1880s.

Carl faced not only the trials that most of the local farmers did, but also he was with only one foot. Carl got along pretty well with that, but farming is tough enough without having such a burden. In addition, two of his children were chronically ill which was a drain, both in terms of expense and worry.

Things were tough for the Williams family and getting worse. They did what they could to stave off the inevitable. They knew that it would be just a matter of time before the bank came for their stock and land.

When the day actually came, Carl just could not handle it. When some men hired by the bank were driving his cattle off down the road, it was just the last straw for Carl Williams. In a futile attempt to stop the whole thing, Carl got into the path of the cattle.

What with all the hollering and carrying on among the men, the normally placid animals got excited and started to run.

Carl never should have gotten in their way. Those heavy and sharp-hooved animals ran right over Carl and inflicted some very serious injuries. Carl Williams died right there on the road. The manner of his death was just one more element of a tragic life.

It was several months later when a tradesman was traveling that road toward Berryville. The hour was growing late and it was well past nightfall. There was, however, more than sufficient moonlight for the man to guide his horse-drawn cart down that road.

Suddenly the tradesman heard the distinct

sound of cattle running. He knew the sound well for he had been a boy on a farm years earlier.

The man's curiosity soon turned to concern as he realized that those cattle were on the same road as he and that they were coming toward him very rapidly. He couldn't figure why anyone would be driving cattle at such an hour. Perhaps, he thought, they were being run by a dog or some other animal.

That speculation came to a halt as the man hurriedly pulled his rig off the road. If there was going to be a bunch of cattle stampeding down that road, he sure didn't want to be on it. He could tell that they were almost upon him by that time.

As the man sat there, reins in hand, he realized that the sounds he was hearing were now coming from that road directly on his left. Yet not one animal was in sight.

As the astonished man watched he saw something he never was to forget. He saw what anyone who has ever seen cattle run, has seen. Leaping up from the ground were little chunks of dirt that would fly into the air, as if thrown from a hoof. Some would arc high in the air, and others would leap a few inches up, then fall back to earth. Fascinated, the man watched those little pieces of dirt fly into the air, accompanied by the thunder of many hooves. He could see it all well, thanks to the full moon of the night.

Then suddenly, the sound and the flying dirt were gone, leaving only the moonlight and silence.

The next occurrence of an odd nature that happened in the following few moments must have taken place when the man's eyes were diverted back to his horse. When he glanced back to the road, he saw another shocking thing. There on the ground was lying, fully visible in the moonlight, the crumpled and twisted body of a man with only one foot.

 The impatient snort from his horse galvanized the tradesman to leap to the ground to investigate. Racing to the form lying in the road, the man caught his foot in a tree root, catapulting him end over end. In that couple of seconds, the body disappeared. One moment it was there; the next, it was gone.

A thoroughly shaken tradesman climbed into his cart and continued on to Berryville. To see the flying dirt from the feet of cattle that weren't there, and then to see the body of a man that subsequently disappeared was almost more than he could handle.

During the drive on into Berryville, the tradesman stopped a couple of times and listened closely to see if he could once again hear the sounds of hooves in the night. He neither heard nor saw anything out of the ordinary the rest of the trip.

While conducting his business the next day in Berryville, the man told of his experience of the previous night. It was then that he learned that that was the spot where Carl Williams had died under the hooves of his cattle.

Frequently over the following years, others heard those thundering hooves on moonlit nights. A couple of times, the trampled body of a one-footed man would also be seen.

The last sighting of the body was supposed to have been in 1903 with one recent exception. That was in 1972 when it was seen again, almost seventy years later and almost a hundred years after Carl Williams met his tragic death on a dirt road.

CHAPTER XIII

ROLAND'S SURPRISE

Roland Draman had owned his farm near Hickory Hill, Missouri for quite a few years before he made an amazing discovery about that place. He never would have found that out, but by sheer accident.

It was in the spring when Roland made his discovery. It was one of those warm spring days that can go bad on a moment's notice, and Roland was out mushroom hunting. Roland had no reason to think of rain when he took off from the house for the patch of timber east of a thirty-five acre field he had close by the house.

He had fall plowed that field a few months earlier, so the soil was nice and mellow. He knew that he'd better get his mushroomin' done because spring work was going to be in full swing pretty soon. While Roland was in that timber, he failed to notice those storm clouds building up in the west. In fact, the first few drops of rain hit the trees above his head before he realized he was in for a soaking.

All thoughts of mushrooms just sort of melted away as Roland headed off for the house. That spring rain can be chilly enough to put a fellow a couple of months back into winter and Roland had no appetite for getting soaked over a bunch of mushrooms.

That sprint across the field degenerated into wading through mud in a few moments. That plowed ground got sticky real fast in the hard rain. He was sloughing along pretty mad  about the whole thing. The rain stopped about as fast as it had started, but the damage was done. Roland had about already ruined a good pair of shoes and was wet and mad.

Our now-soaked mushroom hunter forgot about all that, however, as he saw what was going on out there in the middle of that field he was walking in. There was a rectangle about eight  feet on a side in which the ground was very dry. It wasn't a matter of being a little less muddy. It was just flat-out bone dry. He knew that what he was seeing couldn't be, but there it was. Roland sifted some of the dirt through his fingers and let it fall to the earth. It was powdery and dry as the entire field had been an hour earlier.

No amount of standing there looking at the ground yielded any answer as to how that could be. Rain doesn't go around skipping eight-foot square patches. Roland was alone in that field and knew that there had been no one there who could have laid something on that spot, then left. He knew there was not wind enough to have carried away a large sheet of anything that could have been lying there. It was all just plain impossible, yet there it was.

Twice Roland started to leave, but he retraced his steps again to study that section of ground. It was the dangest thing he had ever seen!

Roland finally returned to the house but re-solved never to tell anyone about the incident. He figured it was bad enough to have such a crazy thing happen on his place without making a fool of himself by telling anyone else about it.

He also resolved to go back to that spot the next time it rained. He was sure enough going to check to see if it would happen again.

Being spring and all, it didn't take long to wait. It wasn't but three or four days later it came up with a good shower again. Roland waited for the ground to get good and soaked up. By the time the rain was over, that field was a sea of mud again. Roland donned his buckle-up overshoes and trudged out to that spot. Sure enough, that same rectangular spot was dry as could be. All that time, he had owned that place and had never known that such an odd thing was going on. He just hadn't had occasion to go out into that field in the rain before.

Finding that it happened the second time didn't do anything, of course, toward explaining why or how such a thing could be.

With that confirmation of the situation, Roland decided to enlist some help in attempting to explain the whole mess. He decided to seek the aid of his young neighbor, Keith Mann.

Keith had been off to Agricultural College. Roland sure knew that he couldn't figure it out himself, and maybe Keith could.

Roland asked Keith to come over to his house the next time it rained good after the ground was good and dry. He refused to confide in his neighbor why he wanted him over; he just got him to agree to come. Roland wasn't about to spill the beans unless that dry spot actually showed up again.

Well, the next rain came about ten days later. Keith came as he had agreed and wanted to know what his visit was supposed to be all about.

Roland took Keith to the fence about two hundred yards from where he had seen the spot and asked Keith to examine the field well and see what he could see out there.

Keith's enthusiasm for standing in the rain, looking out over an empty field was less than unrestrained. He felt like he was standing there getting soaked to play some silly game. But he went along with it and allowed to Roland that he didn't see anything out there but bare ground and lots of rain.

While it was still raining, the pair then trudged out to that spot where Keith saw what Roland had seen twice before. He was, of course, shocked at what he saw. College or no college,  he had absolutely no idea what could have caused such a thing. Keith took a real interest in the situation and did a little investigation on his own. His questioning there in the neighborhood led him to an old-timer. That old man recalled that many years earlier a farmer had been in that field discing with horses. Somehow, he was working on the disc and got run over by it when the horses apparently spooked over something.

The old timer went on to tell that the farmer's wife saw the horses come roaring back to the barn without her husband. Her investigation led her to the field where she found him, mortally injured. The poor woman was unable to move him by herself. Since it was threatening rain, she ran back to the house to get a canvas to cover him.

She then ran back to the house to summon help. When help arrived, the man was dead. Her only comfort was that her attempts to keep him dry had allowed him to die in comfort. Those who came to help could do little more than move the body to the house, from which it was then taken to town.

In due course, the wife died also, some said of a broken heart. Apparently, the woman's ghost then still saw to the comfort of the farmer by preventing the rain from falling on that spot. An invisible ghost with a canvas cover that can't be seen still kept that little spot of ground dry in that little field every time it rained.

CHAPTER XIV

OLD LACE

When Lydia Parkinson, who lived near Mount Ida, Arkansas, was seventeen years old back in 1909 she was allowed to take the family's buggy out by herself at night.

That privilege was very much appreciated because Lydia had a friend whose name we don't know, but who lived between Mount Ida and Black Springs. Apparently the two girls spent a lot of time together.

There had been lots of spooky stories circulating around about the old Jarvis house on that road, but Lydia had never paid any attention to those stories since she never had believed in ghosts, even as a child. The need to go past the old Jarvis place on her way to her friends didn't

bother her at all. She was confident that the tales of ghostly images and floating lights around that house were simply fabrications.

It was getting a bit late in the evening that September night in '09 when Lydia was driving along the road past the Jarvis house.

At first she assumed the white image she saw up ahead was simply a break in the trees with the lighter background showing through that dense grove. She remembered, later, having seen that image when she was yet well down the road but then dismissing it.

Lydia was almost upon the figure when she realized that it wasn't a break in the trees at all, but a wispy image of a girl about her own age, and she was motioning with her arm as if to ask Lydia to stop.

Apparently the horse either stopped on his own or Lydia involuntarily and inadvertently pulled back on the reins to stop him. Whatever the reason, Lydia Parkinson found herself stopped there by the old Jarvis house staring at a girl's figure that seemed to change back and forth between an ill-defined image and a clear one of a young lady.

It took a couple of minutes for Lydia to realize that this was a really strange situation. People don't just change back and forth from a clear image to a whispy one.

Suddenly the girl spoke and asked Lydia her name. Without thinking, Lydia answered and asked the figure in front of her who she was.

The answer that Lydia got fully convinced her that this was no place to be alone in the night.

"I have no name for I am without a body. I should like your's, if I may."

Even as she spoke those words in such an old-fashioned way, the girl on the road reached for the hand-hold on the side of the buggy. Her beautiful lace shawl draped from her arm almost like a delicate waterfall.

This was too much. With a scream, Lydia brought the reins down roughly on the back of her horse, causing him to lurch in his harness, spinning the figure around there on the road as the buggy leaped forward.

 Lydia had gotten strict orders not to run the horse at all and to trot it only for brief periods of time. Those instructions were all but forgotten as she raced the entire way back to the house as fast as her horse would go. She thought she had troubles a lot more serious than a possible scolding from her father.

A couple of times during that wild ride Lydia thought for sure that she was going to tip the buggy over, or at least lose a wheel.

Even in her wild flight, Lydia tried to recall her father's complaints of a few evenings earlier about the high price of buggy wheels.

Fortunately, however, Lydia arrived at the house with the buggy all in one piece.

Without even tring the horse up, Lydia ran into the safety of the house and the reassuring warmth of the kerosene lamps inside.

Lydia breathlessly tried to explain to her parents why she had arrived in such a dither. She told them that she was sure that what she had seen was a ghost.

All that, of course, was met with some indulgent chuckles by her father who teased her a bit for her fear of ghosts.

When Mr. Parkinson went out to put the horse away, Lydia followed him out. She wanted to be there to defend herself when her father discovered that the horse was all out of breath and lathered up from his exertion. She had lucked out pretty well so far and didn't want to push her luck.

It was Mr. Parkinson who first saw the piece of torn lace hung up on the end of the cinch rod on the back of the buggy. In the semi-darkness of the lot, that piece of lace looked white and fresh. When they got inside, however, it proved to be old and yellowed. It was, in fact, so fragile that it almost fell apart as Lydia and her parents handled it.

"Why, Mother. It's the same lace the girl on the road wore. I remember seeing it very well because she was so close to me and the lace is so pretty."

Apparently, the Parkinsons never did figure out exactly what Lydia saw along the road that night. She was convinced until the day she died in 1964 that what she saw was a ghost.

Lydia's account of that September night is still in her diary which rests securely today in a safety deposit box in a bank in Little Rock along with the fragile remains of a piece of lace that was already old back in 1909.

CHAPTER XV

THE FATAL CARD

I t was sometime in the early 1800s when the Stevens family first came to Marion County and bought land. The original Stevens lived here the rest of his life until 1882. The family eventually proved to be long-time residents, staying on the same place for five generations.

The son of one of the fourth generation lives today in Yellville and is pushing 90 so the family has a long history in the area.

In 1898 the Stevens had a situation there on

their place that got them into this book.

The whole thing would never have happened if
Rodney Stevens, the grandson of the original
settler, hadn't had a weakness for playing cards,
particularly poker. Rodney's habit cost the
family dearly. When he inherited the place in
1897, it was a large farm with fine
buildings and equipment. It also
had some of the finest livestock
in the county. Three generations of
hard work had paid off, and things were looking
pretty good for Rodney and Mrs. Stevens.

That is, things were looking pretty good until
one evening in '98 when Rodney had a little
poker game going there in the parlor. Mrs.
Stevens didn't approve of those games, but Rodney was an incurable poker player and insisted
on his occasional game. She started out early in
their marriage objecting to it all, but she soon
found that it didn't do any good to fight it. She

eventually learned just to go to bed and to hope
for the best. Some mornings she would awaken
to find themselves a few dollars richer, and
sometimes a few dollars poorer.

Rodney's fascination with poker had, until that
particular night, never led him to excessive or
reckless betting. Maybe it was the home brew
that night, or maybe fate had simply decided it
was time to deal Rodney a bum hand. Whatever
the reason, he got way in over his head that
night. The cards weren't running right and
every bluff failed. Within a couple of hours after
getting started, Rodney had lost lots of cash. By
midnight his livestock was gone, and by the
time a shocked and dazed Rodney Stevens quit
playing that night, he found his friends taking
home his money and several IOU's. Those IOU's
that were so easily written in the heat of the
game bore down on Rodney like a heavy weight
because he knew it would take most of his

equipment to cover them. To watch his friends gleefully pocket those IOU's was almost more than Rodney could bear.

The crowning disaster had happened just before he quit when he had a full house, Kings high, in a game of seven card stud. He was going up against what appeared to be another full house, tens high. Rodney's opponent had been a heavy winner and had plenty of money to bet with. Rodney was sure the fellow had that full house, ten high, and that that's what he was betting on.

And that's exactly what his opponent had, three tens and a pair of sixes. The man was right proud of those cards and apparently had no idea that Rodney had a full house also.

Much of Rodney's full house in "down cards" and it looked all in the world like he had a pair or two and was bluffing it.

Rodney wasn't bluffing it, jowever. He had those three Kings and a pair of dueces cold by the sixth card and had every expectation of getting back all the money he had lost that evening.

Rodney's last card was a three which didn't help him a bit. But he figured that with his hand, he didn't need any help. He had it made.

The last card down, however, had a profound effect on his opponent's hand. He had two tens and a six showing. His "hole" cards were a ten and a six going into that last "down" card proved to be the ten of diamonds.

Well, now, that ten of diamonds proved to make a whole new ballgame out of what was already a good hand. That fellow now had four tens that would beat any full house at all. He knew that Rodney would have to have three Kings in the "hole" to beat him, and that was highly unlikely.

Since both men now had real good hands, it quickly became a matter of high bets, some hefty raises, and more bets. Both men were firmly convince they had a barn-burner and both felt they were on the verge of becoming rich.

There has to be a loser in every poker hand, of course. When Rodney's opponent turned over his "hole" cards and re-vealed his four tens, Rodney's world came crashing down around him. Sud-denly his money was gone, his fine livestock were all owed to other people, and most of the good machinery out in the shed was covering those IOU's.

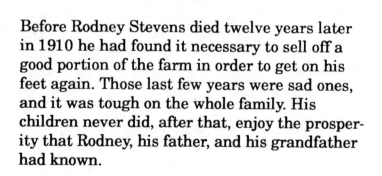

Before Rodney Stevens died twelve years later in 1910 he had found it necessary to sell off a good portion of the farm in order to get on his feet again. Those last few years were sad ones, and it was tough on the whole family. His children never did, after that, enjoy the prosper-ity that Rodney, his father, and his grandfather had known.

It was from Rodney's grandson that I learned this story. He told me that even he, the fifth generation after the founder, was affected. He would have liked to have gotten the old home place but there simply wasn't enough left when his unlucky grandfather died to keep it intact.

That just goes to show you what can happen when a man heavy into poker has a bad night. I could be settin' up there in the home place right now instead of in this crummy apartment if it wasn't for that card game that night."

"Yes," I observed. "A card game that was over with almost a hundred years ago still has its effect, I guess."

I was wondering however, what all this had to do about the ghost story that I had been told this fellow knew.

"Well, It really aint't over yet. At least, there's still something goin' on there in that house that came from that game."

"What's that?" I asked.

"You may think it's crazy, but it's true and it's been true ever since my grandfather died in 1910. There hasn't been a deck of cards in that house that will keep the ten of diamonds."

"What do you mean?"

"I mean that the ten of diamonds always gets lost or torn as soon as anyone takes a deck into that house. It's been that way for a long time, ever since Grandpa died."

Everbody has always figured that Grandpa's ghost has been in that house and just can't stand the sight of the card that cost him his fine farm. It was the ten of diamonds that made the hand that beat Grandpa's full house, you know."

"You don't suppose," I asked, "that some family member had been doing that for a joke?"

"No, 'cause there have been things that prove otherwise. For instance, one day my uncle brought a brand new deck home. It set around a while before they opened it. When they did, they found the ten of diamonds had a bad ink smear on the back of it so it couldn't be used.

Another time, there had been some company staying at the house. The lady of this couple had three decks of cards in her luggage that no one knew about. She got those out so they could play some cards and the ten of diamonds was missing from every one of them."

Apparently, a poker game played almost a hundred years ago isn't quite over yet. It seems that one of the players has it in for the ten of diamonds.

CHAPTER XVI

THE WARNING SIGN

The story of the ghost of Harold Henning is one that comes to us from fairly recent times. It took place in the 1940s which makes it a bit more contemporary than most ghost stories.

Several people saw the ghost, they just didn't know that's what it was when they saw it.

It all started in the early spring of either 1947 or 1948, depending on which one of the relatives is telling the tale. Whatever year it happened, it was in the early spring and some warm, rainy days had caused considerable flooding that year.

Harold Henning's daughter, Donna, was going to school at the University of Arkansas and was on her way home to spend a few days during a break in her classes. She was riding with some other students from the area around Russell-ville who all came in the one car. Donna had missed coming home for Christmas so was looking forward to seeing her parents.

Those college kids were busy comparing notes about what they would be doing for the next few

days. Donna was all enthused about having
a chance to make some good
old home-made candy.

The kids had gotten close
to town and the driver
had apparently gotten
a little heavy-footed
on the gas, going along
at a pretty good clip.
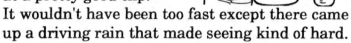
It wouldn't have been too fast except there came
up a driving rain that made seeing kind of hard.

They were on that hard road heading for town.
Apparently that heavy rain had finished the
work started by the spring thaws and Lost
Creek had eaten away a good-sized chunk of the
road. In fact, most of the lane the car with those
kids was on had been washed out for about a
twelve to fifteen foot stretch. There was no way
those kids would have seen that in time as
heavy as the rain was and as hard as it was to
see.

Well, before they got to that unseen hole in the
road, however, the figure of a man suddenly
materialized out of the fog and rain holding a
large sign reading "SLOW DOWN, ROAD
OUT".

In the single second that it took to go past that
man, Donna Henning recognized him to be her
father. She wasn't surprised to see her father

out there serving to warn people of the danger ahead. He was that kind of man. She was awfully surprised, however, to see him standing there in a simple blue workshirt, but no coat. It was way too chilly that day to be out without a coat, especially as bad as it was raining.

Donna whirled around in her seat to look around so she could figure out why her dad was out in such weather without warm clothing.

"Why, that's my father out there. That was him holding the sign."

"My gosh!" exclaimed a friend. "He sure isn't dressed to be out on a day like this one is."

"I know. But let's not stop now. Let's just get around the washout here he warned us about. I'll come back with a coat for him."

"Wow!", the driver said. "Look at the hole in the road here. I'm sure glad your dad was there to tell us about this. Look, we can just barely get around that giant hole. We'd wrecked, for sure, if I hadn't gotten slowed down in time."

Donna and the others stared wide-eyed at the hole in the road that could have been the end of all of them.

"Hurry up", Donna urged. "Our place is just a few hundred feet down the road. I'll get in my my brother's car and take a coat back to Dad."

By then the car had gotten to the gate at the
entrance to the Henning homestead.

Donna was anxious to get into the house to get
something for her dad to wear. She burst into
the front porch letting the door slam behind her
and dropped her bag there on the floor by the
door.

All that racket
brought Mrs. Henn-
ing's sister to the door
to greet Donna.
Donna's Aunt Sarah
lived not too far away,
but she and Donna's
mother never had
been real close, so

Donna was surprised to see her aunt there at the house. That surprise soon changed to apprehension when Donna could tell from her aunt's face that something was awfully wrong.

"It's your father, Donna."

It came to Donna immediately. She knew her father must have suffered another bad heart attack. However, even as she started to say the words, asking if he had, the look on her Aunt Sarah's face told her that the news was even worse.

But then, with a surge of relief, Donna knew it couldn't be. She had just seen her father not three minutes earlier holding that sign down by the creek. She knew that he had just saved her and her companions from a bad car wreck.

"What is it, Aunt Sarah?" What's the matter?"

"Your father, Donna. He died this afternoon of a really bad heart attack. The body is in the bedroom now. The funeral director is on his way now and should be here shortly. Your mother is in the kitchen with the doctor. She's been waiting for you to get home.

Donna couldn't figure out why her Aunt Sarah was saying those words. She knew that's all they were, just words. She had seen her father just moments before. So had her friends.

Her words of protest to her aunt were stilled by her mother entering the room from the kitchen. The doctor was with her. Donna knew from the look on their faces that Aunt Sarah wasn't simply pulling some mean and cruel trick. Her father was dead.

Neither Donna nor her mother could speak at first. The doctor asked Donna if she wanted to see her father's body before the funeral director got there.

"Yes, please".

When Donna entered the bedroom to see the body, she was shocked to see her father lying there in the very same tan trousers and light blue workshirt she had seen him in not ten minutes earlier out on the road.

"Papa died early this afternoon, Honey." Her mother told Donna who was standing there in shock and confusion.

"He was working on trying to fix an old radio down in the basement in his shop.

"You should know, Honey, that he thought of you children up to the very end."

Donna ignored her mother's questioning look and resolved to tell her later of how her father had saved her and the others in the car from a bad wreck. She knew then that it was her father's ghost that was out on the road holding up that sign.

CHAPTER XVII

THE BOY

This story came out of a hunting incident from back in 1938. The situation was well investigated at the time by the follows involved and with the aid of two physics professors from the University of Missouri.

The three fellows who first saw the ghost had absolutely no idea that it was a ghost until they had talked about it for a while.

The trio were at a deer blind north of Cassville, Missouri, Barry County. The blind didn't belong to any of the three. In fact, they didn't even know who it belonged to. While they didn't have permission to use that blind, they went ahead anyway. They figured it was a good place to hunt squirrels from.

Since the blind was very small, only Kent Willis, of the three, was actually in it. The other two fellows, Max Hardin and Dennis Young were standing on the ground near the blind.

It was in the fall and the dried and dead leaves covered the ground. Those leaves being down not only made it easier to see up in the trees, but they also rustled loudly as the squirrels would play in them. Even the little chipmunks seemed to make as much noise as a deer in those dry leaves.

Suddenly Max and Dennis fell silent as they saw Kent motioning to them. Kent had heard the distinctive rustle of the leaves caused by a squirrel hopping through the woods. Kent was trying to determine where that noise was coming from.

Then, suddenly, Kent uttered a short expletive under his breath as he spied a young lad of about twelve or thirteen strolling along toward the blind. He thought that the boy would certainly scare away any squirrels that might happen to be in the immediate neighborhood. He started to say something to his companions about how the squirrel hunting would be over

for a good fifteen or twenty minutes now that
that d---- kid had messed thing up.

Kent didn't get that said, for just then he
noticed the fox trotting alongside the boy. That
fox was not only failing to run away from the
boy but was actually tagging alongside of him.

Now, Kent Willis had seen some odd things in
the woods before, but he had never seen a fox
tag along with a person like a cat or a dog
would do. But that's exactly what he was
seeing. The pair was no more than fifty yards
away from the blind by this time and their path
promised to pass right under that blind and by
the three men.

Kent was so surprised at that sight, he had to
assure himself that what he saw was for real.
Turning to Max who was right below him, Kent
urged Max to look out there.

"Hey, Max, look out there and tell me what you
see."

A little bit mystified, Max did just that. He saw
the lad right away and was turning back up to
Kent to tell him they had some company, when
he saw the fox also. He saw the same thing that
Kent had. That fox was tagging along after the
boy like a cat would.

"What the..........!" Max whispered. "Who's that,
and how come he's got a fox? Foxes don't do
that."

Max quickly nudged Dennis to get him to look
at that strange thing.

Unlike Max, Dennis already had some idea of
what was going on since Max had made those
comments about a person and a fox. Then that,
too, was exactly what Dennis saw when he
looked over there.

Soon the odd pair was passing the blind and
continuing on down the path. Kent shouted to
the lad.

"Say, how'd ya ever get a pet fox?" That apparently, was the first time
the boy or the fox knew they

were not the only ones in the woods that day. The lad stopped and looked back toward the blind where those words came from. Then he simply walked over to a small tree about four or

five inches in diameter and disappeared.

Now, a young boy can hide behind a big tree alright, but there isn't a person alive who can hide behind one only four or five inches in diameter. Dennis sat speechless for a moment or two before looking at the other two fellows who had been watching it all.

The three fellows all looked at each other, each one reluctant to be the first to speak after what they had seen.

Max was the first to suggest they go over to the

tree to see what was going on. So the three of them went over there and carefully inspected that little tree the boy had disappeared behind. It looked all in the world like an ordinary tree, but there was no sight of the lad.

The trio stood there discussing the situation for several minutes before one of them suggested they had a ghost on their hands. Neither of the other two could come up with any better explanation.

Some investigation by Kent Willis revealed that the little glen where that deer blind was had been a cemetery at one time. In fact Kent Willis found a couple of stones in a portion of that little glen that had grown over in brush and was almost impossible to get to because of the grape vines and elderberry bushes.

A physics professor friend of Dennis's also came to Barry County to look into the whole thing. He took some measurements and photographs, but could come up with nothing anymore convincing than the ghost theory. That little tree proved to be 4.35 inches in diameter at a point five feet from the ground and a little over five inches in diameter at the base, certainly not enough for a mortal boy to hide behind.

CHAPTER XVIII

THIN ICE

It was in the late 1920s when Arlo and Bernice Woods moved onto their little farm on the outskirts of Eldon, Missouri.

While most farmers traditionally moved on March 1st, the Woods couple and their three children did so in the middle of December. The farm had been vacant so they didn't have to go through the business of waiting for previous occupants to move off.

Lilly, the eleven-year-old daughter was really looking forward to Christmas. She had dropped enough hints about "really needing a pair of ice skates for sure" that year.

Lilly had seen a picture of a beautiful lady on ice skates, and she wanted awfully bad to learn how to skate.

"You know, Daddy, with that pond bein' right almost outside our back door, now, it would be perfect for skating."

Mr. Woods' smiling response about "waiting to see what Santa brought on Christmas" convinced Lilly she could almost count on those skates.

Christmas brought both good news and bad for Lilly. She got her skates alright, but it hadn't been cold enough to freeze that pond. The little ring of ice around the edges was a far cry from enough ice to support Lilly and her new skates.

It seemed to be a warmer winter than usual. It was almost New Year's and there was still lots of open water on the pond and not nearly enough ice for Lilly to try out her new skates.

Lilly's complaining about that situation one night right after Christmas prompted Mrs. Woods to offer a little encouragement.

"Just be patient, Lilly. We'll get a cold snap that will freeze that pond over real good."

Mrs. Woods appeared to be right. When Lilly got up the next morning, she could tell it had gotten cold in the night.

When she glanced out at the pond, she couldn't tell if it was frozen or not since the little dam hid the surface of the pond from view there at the house.

Lilly was busy pulling her overshoes on to go out to inspect that pond when she glanced out of the window again.

"Oh, Mother, look!"

"What's the matter, Lilly?"

"Nothing's the matter! Oh, look! there's a little
girl out there skating. You can't see the ice, but
you can see her, and she is really skating aong.
So, there's gotta be enough ice now. Oh, goodie!
There is ice now."

"There sure is, Honey. That little girl looks to be
about your age. Maybe you will have a chance
to meet her and some of the other children in
the neighborhood, now."

"Oh, look, Mommie."

"What now?"

"There are two chil-
dren out there. See,
there's a boy too. He
looks a lot older
though. I'll bet he is
in high school. Who
do you suppose they
are?"

"I'm sure they are
some of the neighbors,
Lilly. You best get out

there so's you can meet them."

"Okay, Mommie, I'm going. Can I bring them in for hot chocolate if they want to come?"

"Sure, Honey. Go and have fun."

Bernice smiled as her eager little daughter almost forgot her skates in her hurry to get out to the pond to try them out and to meet some of the neighboring children.

It wasn't but a few minutes before Mrs. Woods' motherly instincts led her to slip on her husband's heavy winter coat to walk over by the pond to be sure Lilly was alright. She didn't really have any serious concerns, since the ice was obviously thick enough to hold up those two people out there, but it would be a pleasant little jaunt.

The first thing that Bernice noticed when she stepped out of the door was that it wasn't nearly as cold out as she would have expected. That heavy winter coat was actually too much to wear. It was as warm as it had been for the several previous days. She wondered how the pond could have frozen so well if it had been that warm all night.

Bernice dismissed the whole question.
Obviously it had, indeed, been cold enough.
Apparently it had warmed up again quickly as
soon as the sun came up.

The next thing that Mrs. Woods saw was her
daughter coming back down the path toward
her with a very strange look on her face. It was
a look that Bernice had never seen before.

Bernice met Lilly and asked her why she wasn't
up there on the pond, skating.

"As much as you've looked forward to this ice-
skating business, you had best take advantage
of the ice now. We could have a real mild winter
and you might not be able to do much skating
this year."

That's all it took. Lilly's tears came gushing
forth as if she had had a hard time holding
them back.

Between Lilly's sobs, Mrs. Woods learned that
those weren't tears of disappointment or pain.
They were tears of fear.

"Why, what's the matter, Honey? What are you afraid of?"

Lilly could no longer control her sobs and could only point to the pond, yet holding her mother's skirt as if she was afraid her mother would leave her.

Events had gotten so strange by this time that Mrs. Woods quickly walked the remaining few yards up the rise where she would be able to look out across the pond. She was speculating that those children had been cruel to Lilly for some reason. She certainly wasn't going to have people coming onto their place and teasing her children. She'd give those two a piece of her mind!

The strangest sight that Mrs. Woods had ever seen or was ever to see greeted her as she stepped up onto that little dam. There was not a child in sight, either on or off of skates.

Furthermore, that pond wasn't frozen over at all. The same thin ring of ice was around the edge, not even thick enough to support the weight of a decent-sized duck, much less that of a child. The pond hadn't frozen that night at all.

Bernice stood there on that balmy late December morning for several minutes, trying to come to grips with what she was seeing.

Then, quickly, Bernice turned, walked back to where Lilly was sitting down on the ground, refusing to look toward the pond at all. Bernice took her daughter's hand and the two of them went to the kitchen to talk.

No one in the family ever used the word "ghost" for fear of alarming the smaller children, but both Lilly and her parents knew that they shared their new home with someone else.

That elusive pair was seen several times over the next few years, in both winter and summer. The last reported sighting was in the fall of 1934 when Mr. and Mrs. Woods were out in the woods and saw those two children playing some sort of running game high in the treetops.

No one in the family ever found out anything about the history of the farm that would shed any light on who those children were.

Lilly is now no longer an exuberant eleven-year-old. Her hair is as white as the snow she used to play in. Lilly lives with her son in St. Louis. She hasn't gone ice skating for over half a century now, but she has never forgotten that December morning back in the late 1920s on her family's farm in Miller County.

EPILOGUE

:

So, Lilly Woods was not to meet her
neighbors,.......at least not in this world.

And, what of Carl Williams? Does he, yet today,
journey through time to lose his life yet again
and again 'neath the thundering hooves of that
herd of cattle south of Eureka Springs?

Somewhere an old Indian who never quite
accepted the tools of modern living watches over
the church garden near the little town of Mansfield. Does that garden, in the still of the night,
get tended now and then by an old man with a
turtle- shell hoe?

And throughout our beautiful Ozarks, things
happen yet today.............things born of the
passions, loves, and lives of folks from generations ago.

Oh, but if these mountains and hills could
speak!!

INDEX

Chapter Titles are
in capital letters.

A

B

C

D

E

F

J

L

M

O

W

Y

YEARS

Need a Gift?

for
• Birthday • Father's Day •
• Anniversary • Christmas•

Turn Page For Order Form
(Order Now While Supply Lasts!)

TO ORDER COPIES OF:
Ghosts of the Ozarks

Please send me _____ copies at $9.95 each plus $2.00 S/H each. (Make checks payable to **QUIXOTE PRESS**.)

Name _____

Street _____

City _____ State _____ Zip _____

SEND ORDERS TO:
QUIXOTE PRESS
1854-345th Avenue
Wever IA 52658
800-571-2665

TO ORDER COPIES OF:
Ghosts of the Ozarks

Please send me _____ copies at $9.95 each plus $2.00 S/H each. (Make checks payable to **QUIXOTE PRESS**.)

Name _____

Street _____

City _____ State _____ Zip _____

SEND ORDERS TO:
QUIXOTE PRESS
1854-345th Avenue
Wever IA 52658
800-571-2665